The Healthy

Alkaline Diet

Guide

Quick and Easy
Alkaline to Improve your
Metabolism

Sam Carter

By reading this document, the reader agrees that under no circumstances is the author responsible for any losses, direct or indirect, which are incurred as a result of the use of information contained within this document, including, but not limited to, — errors, omissions, or inaccuracies.

Table of Contents

Cabbage & Potato Hash

Servings: 2

Total Time: 15 minutes

Ingredients

- 2 tablespoons olive oil
- 2 small sunchokes, shredded
- 1 cup red cabbage, thinly shredded
- 2 small yellow potatoes, grated
- ¼ cup yellow onion, finely diced
- 1 teaspoon Himalayan salt
- 1 teaspoon rosemary, chopped
- 1 teaspoon black pepper, crushed
- 2 tablespoons green onions, thinly sliced

Directions

1. Heat oil in a small skillet over medium heat. Add sunchokes, cabbage, potatoes and onion.

2. Cook 10 minutes, stirring frequently.

3.   Season with salt, rosemary and pepper. Cook another 5 minutes.

4.   Garnish with green onions.

Mediterranean Tofu Scramble

Servings: 2

Total Time: 15 minutes

Ingredients

- 3 tablespoons olive oil
- 2 cups spinach, chopped
- 1 shallot, thinly sliced
- ½ cup sun dried tomatoes, thinly sliced
- 8 ounces extra firm tofu
- ¼ cup black olives, sliced
- 1 teaspoon oregano
- 1 teaspoon basil
- ½ teaspoon Himalayan salt
- ¼ teaspoon turmeric
- 3 tablespoons water
- 3-4 fresh basil leaves, thinly sliced

Directions

1.   Heat oil in medium skillet over medium-high heat. Add shallot, spinach and sun-dried tomatoes. Cook 5 minutes.

2.   Add tofu to the pan and break up with a spoon. Cook 2 minutes and add olives.

3.   In a small bowl, combine oregano, basil, salt, turmeric and water. Add to pan and cook 5 minutes or until liquid is evaporated.

4.   Garnish with basil leaves.

Tomato Toast

Servings: 2

Total Time: 30 minutes

Ingredients

- ½ small sweet onion, finely diced
- ½ cup sun dried tomatoes, diced small
- 10 cherry tomatoes, quartered
- 1 garlic clove, grated
- 1 teaspoon oregano
- 1 cup spinach, thinly sliced
- 2 tablespoons olive oil, divided
- 1 tablespoon lemon juice
- 2 teaspoons Himalayan salt
- 1 teaspoon black pepper
- 4 slices sprouted bread, toasted
- 1 tablespoon green onion, thinly sliced

Directions

1.   Preheat oven to 400°F/205°C.

2.   On a baking tray lined with parchment paper, combine onion, sun dried tomatoes, cherry tomatoes and garlic. Drizzle with 1 tablespoon olive oil and add oregano and 1 teaspoon of the salt. Toss to coat and make sure mixture is spread evenly over the pan.

3.   Place tray in the oven and roast for 25 minutes, flipping once or until tomatoes are soft and slightly caramelized.

4.   In a small bowl, combine spinach, remaining olive oil, lemon juice, remaining salt and pepper. Mix well to combine and set aside for 15 minutes.

5.   Place spinach mixture on top of toast slices, top with tomatoes and garnish with green onion.

Spicy Tofu Breakfast Bake

Servings: 2

Total Time: 20 minutes

Ingredients

- 1 teaspoon olive oil
- ½ red onion
- 3 garlic cloves, minced
- 1 green bell pepper
- 1 jalapeno, seeded and diced
- ½ teaspoon smoked paprika
- ½ teaspoon cumin
- 3 tablespoons tomato purée
- 1 cup diced tomatoes
- 2 cups spinach
- 1 teaspoon Himalayan salt
- 8 ounces silken tofu
- 1 tablespoon nutritional yeast
- 2 tablespoons cilantro, chopped

Directions

1.   In a large skillet, heat olive oil over medium-low heat. Add onion, garlic, bell pepper, jalapeno, paprika and cumin. Cook for 5 minutes.

2.   Add the tomato purée and diced tomatoes to the pan, reduce heat and let simmer for 10 minutes. Stir in spinach and salt.

3.   Add tofu, breaking up gently with a spoon. Sprinkle with nutritional yeast and cook 3 more minutes. Garnish with cilantro and serve.

Coconut Granola

Servings: 2

Total Time: 5 minutes

Ingredients

- 1 cup oats
- 1/3 cup puffed rice
- ¼ cup walnuts, crushed
- ¼ cup shredded, unsweetened coconut
- 1 tablespoon pumpkin seeds
- ½ teaspoon vanilla extract
- 2 tablespoons raw honey
- 1 teaspoon cinnamon
- 1 teaspoon coconut oil

Directions

1. Heat oil in a medium skillet over medium-low heat. Add all other ingredients and toss to coat.

2. Cook for 4 minutes, stirring constantly and being sure it does not burn.

3.   Transfer to a bowl and let cool before using.

Beet Breakfast Hash

Servings: 2

Total Time: 20 minutes

Ingredients

- 1 teaspoon olive oil
- 1 onion, diced
- 1 sweet potato, shredded
- 1 large beet, shredded
- 6 ounces firm tofu, cubed
- 6 ounces firm tofu, cubed
- 1 tablespoon coconut aminos
- 1 teaspoon Himalayan salt
- 1 teaspoon black pepper, crushed
- 1 tablespoon parsley, chopped

Directions

1.   Heat olive oil in a medium skillet over medium-high heat. Add onion and cook for 5 minutes before adding the sweet potato and beet.

2.   Cook another 10 minutes and then add tofu, coconut aminos, salt and pepper.

3.   Sauté another 5 minutes, toss with the parsley and serve.

Citrus Breakfast Salad

Servings: 2

Total Time: 5 minutes

Ingredients

- 1 persimmon fruit, sliced
- 1 blood orange, sliced into segments
- ¼ cup pomegranate seeds
- 1 tablespoon almonds, toasted and crushed
- ½ cup unsweetened yogurt
- 1 tablespoon lime zest
- 1 teaspoon raw honey

Directions

1. Toss together persimmon, blood orange, pomegranate seeds and almonds in a medium bowl. Divide mixture amongst two plates.

2. In a small bowl, whisk together the yogurt, lime zest and honey.

3. Top each plate with the yogurt mixture and serve.

Turmeric Citrus Crepes

Servings: 2

Total Time: 30 minutes

Ingredients

- 1 cup unsweetened almond milk

- 1 egg

- ½ teaspoon vanilla extract

- 1 teaspoon raw honey

- 1 inch piece turmeric, grated

- ½ ginger clove, grated

- ¼ teaspoon cinnamon

- 2 tablespoons lemon zest

- ¾ cup gluten free flour

- 1 teaspoon coconut oil

- 1 cup unsweetened yogurt

- ¼ cup pomegranate seeds

Directions

1.   In a small bowl, whisk together the almond milk, egg, vanilla, honey, turmeric, ginger, cinnamon and lemon zest. Sift in the flour and whisk to combine.

2.   Heat coconut oil in a medium skillet over medium-low heat. Pour in a bit of the batter and swirl around the pan, coating the entire bottom. Cook 4-5 minutes then flip and cook another 5 minutes to create the crepes. Set aside and repeat with remaining batter.

3.   Divide yogurt and pomegranate amongst each crepe and roll before serving.

Sweet Almond Pears

Servings: 2

Total Time: 12 minutes

Ingredients

- 1 tablespoon coconut oil

- 1 pear, quartered

- ½ cup unsweetened almond milk

- 1 teaspoon vanilla extract

- 1 tablespoon mint, roughly chopped

- ¼ teaspoon cinnamon

- ⅛ teaspoon Himalayan salt

- 1 tablespoon almonds, slivered

- 1 tablespoon raisins

Directions

1. In a medium saucepan over medium-low heat, heat coconut oil and sear pears on each side until brown, about 3 minutes per side. Remove and set aside.

2.   Add almond milk, vanilla, mint, cinnamon and salt to the saucepan. Bring to a low simmer and place pears back in the pan for 3 minutes to soak in the almond milk.

3.   Place pears in a serving bowl, pour almond milk on top and top with the almonds and raisins.

Berry Oatmeal

Servings: 1

Total Time: 15 minutes

Ingredients

- ¾ cup unsweetened almond milk

- ¼ cup water

- ½ cup rolled oats

- ¼ teaspoon cinnamon

- ⅛ teaspoon Himalayan salt

- 1 tablespoon almonds, slivered

Berry Jam

- ½ cup raspberries, chopped

- ½ cup frozen blueberries

- 1 lemon, juiced

- ¼ cup chia seeds

Directions

1.   Prepare Berry Jam by placing raspberries, blueberries and lemon juice in a small saucepan over medium heat. Continue

stirring the fruit as it cooks, mashing slightly with the spoon. Once berries have melted and thickened, about 3 minutes, stir in the chia seeds and stir well for another 1 minute. Remove and transfer to sealable bowl or jar. You will only use 1 tablespoon of jam for this recipe, but jam can be used throughout the week for other breakfasts or snacks.

2.   In a medium saucepan, bring almond milk and water to a rolling boil over medium heat. Stir in the oats, cinnamon, salt and almonds and reduce heat to low. Simmer 3-4 minutes or until liquid is absorbed.

3.   Transfer to serving bowl and swirl in 1 tablespoon of the chilled jam. Top with almonds and serve.

Tropical Chia Bowl

Servings: 1

Total Time: 5 minutes plus 8 hours chill time

Ingredients

- 1 cup chia seeds
- 1 cup unsweetened coconut milk
- ¼ teaspoon vanilla extract
- 1 tablespoon flaxseed, ground
- 1 tablespoon raw honey
- 1 cup pineapple, cubed
- 1 mango, peeled and cubed
- 1/3 cup raspberries
- 1/3 cup coconut flakes, toasted
- ½ tablespoon mint, chopped

Directions

1.   In a medium sized bowl or jar, mix the chia seeds, coconut milk, vanilla extract, flaxseeds and honey. Stir well and let sit (covered) overnight in the fridge.

2.   When ready to serve in the morning, add pineapple and mango to a food processor or blender and blend until smooth (add some water if necessary).

3.   In your serving bowl, place a layer of the chia mixture and then a layer of the mango/pineapple mixture. Continue layering until both are used up.

4.   Top with raspberries, coconut and mint before serving.

Tropical Chia Bowl

Servings: 2

Total Time: 1 hour

Ingredients

- 1 cup gluten-free rolled oats
- 1 tablespoon uncooked quinoa
- 1 tablespoon flaxseeds
- ½ cup walnuts
- ¼ cup pepitas
- 2 tablespoons sesame seeds
- ¼ cup coconut flakes
- 1 orange, zested
- ¼ teaspoon Himalayan salt
- ¼ teaspoon cinnamon
- ¼ teaspoon nutmeg
- 1 tablespoon maple syrup
- 1 tablespoon coconut sugar
- 3 tablespoons coconut oil, melted

- ¼ teaspoon vanilla extract

- 2 cups coconut kefir

Directions

1.   Preheat oven to 350°F/180°C and line a baking tray with parchment paper.

2.   In a large bowl, combine the oats, quinoa, flaxseeds, walnuts, pepitas, sesame seeds, coconut flakes, orange zest, salt, cinnamon and nutmeg.

3.   In a small bowl, whisk together the maple syrup, coconut sugar, coconut oil and vanilla extract. Pour over the oats and quinoa mixture and toss well to coat. Spread in an even layer on the prepared baking tray. Bake in the oven for 40 minutes, stirring every 10 minutes to prevent burning.

4.   Remove, let cool for 10 minutes and serve with coconut kefir.

Sweet Potato & Zucchini Hash Brown

Servings: 2

Total Time: 25 minutes

Ingredients

- 2 tablespoons flaxseeds, ground
- 6 tablespoons water
- 1 sweet potato, shredded
- 1 zucchini, shredded
- ½ sweet yellow onion, minced
- 2 tablespoons arrowroot
- ¼ teaspoon Himalayan salt
- ¼ teaspoon black pepper, crushed
- 2 tablespoons coconut oil
- 2 tablespoons unsweetened yogurt
- 2 tablespoons chives, sliced

Directions

1.   In a small bowl, whisk together the flaxseeds and water until well combined. Set aside until a gel forms, about 10 minutes.

2.   Combine the sweet potato, zucchini, onion, flaxseeds gel, arrowroot, salt and pepper in a medium bowl.

3.   Heat coconut oil in a medium sized skillet over medium heat. Form a patty with some of the sweet potato mixture, pressing down slightly and then add it to the skillet. Repeat with remaining sweet potato and zucchini mixture (you may need to make 2 batches depending on your skillet size).

4.   Cook 5 minutes or until slightly browned and then flip and cook another 5 minutes.

5.   Remove and garnish with the yogurt and chives before serving.

Nutty Breakfast Squash

Servings: 2

Total Time: 40 minutes

Ingredients

- 1 acorn squash, sliced in half lengthwise and seeds removed

- ½ tablespoon coconut oil

- ¼ teaspoon Himalayan salt

- 1 cup unsweetened coconut yogurt, divided

- 4 tablespoons oats

- ½ cup raspberries

- 2 dates, pitted and chopped

- 2 tablespoons cashew butter

- 1 tablespoon raw honey

Directions

1. Preheat oven to 400°F/205°C and line a baking tray with parchment paper.

2.   Rub coconut oil on each cut side of the squash and then sprinkle with salt. Place on the baking tray with cut side down and roast in the oven for 30 minutes or until you can pierce the skin with a fork. Cool for 5 minutes.

3.   Take each squash half and fill with half of the yogurt, half of the oats, half the raspberries, 1 date, 1 tablespoon cashew butter and ½ tablespoon honey.

4.   Serve immediately.

Spicy Avocado Breakfast Boat

Servings: 2

Total Time: 20 minutes

Ingredients

- 1 ripe avocado, halved lengthwise and pit removed
- 1 lime, juiced
- 1 tablespoon olive oil
- ½ cup diced red onion
- ½ cup diced red bell pepper
- 1 jalapeno, diced
- 6 ounces firm tofu
- 1 teaspoon nutritional yeast
- ½ teaspoon ground cumin
- ¼ teaspoon oregano
- ⅛ teaspoon ground turmeric
- 1 tablespoon water
- ½ teaspoon black Himalayan salt
- 1 tablespoon fresh chopped cilantro

Directions

1.   Set avocado on two plates and squeeze lime juice on top of each. Set aside.

2.   In a medium skillet over medium heat, add olive oil, red onion, bell pepper and jalapeno. Sauté 5 minutes or until onion and pepper are soft.

3.   Add tofu to the skillet, breaking up with a spoon and cook 3 minutes.

4.   In a small bowl, combine the nutritional yeast, cumin, oregano, turmeric, water and salt. Pour into the skillet and cook 3 more minutes or until the liquid is absorbed.

5.   Divide tofu mixture in half and place on top of the avocado half.

6.   Garnish with cilantro and serve immediately.

Brussel Sprout Hash

Servings: 2

Total Time: 15 minutes

Ingredients

- 1 tablespoon olive oil
- 1 shallot, thinly sliced
- 1 sunchoke, sliced thinly
- 4 brussel sprouts, sliced thinly
- ½ sweet potato, shredded
- ½ teaspoon Himalayan salt
- ½ teaspoon black pepper, crushed
- 1 teaspoon fresh rosemary

Directions

1. Heat olive oil in a medium skillet over medium heat and add the shallot, sunchoke, brussel sprouts and sweet potato.

2. Cook 10 minutes and add salt, pepper and rosemary.

3. Sauté another 5 minutes before removing from heat and serving immediately.

Garden Chickpea Omelet

Servings: 1

Total Time: 25 minutes

Ingredients

- 1/3 cup chickpea flour
- 2 tablespoons flaxseed, ground
- ½ cup water
- 1 tablespoon lemon juice
- 1 teaspoon tahini
- ½ teaspoon Himalayan salt
- ½ teaspoon black pepper, crushed
- ¼ teaspoon turmeric
- ¼ teaspoon oregano
- ¼ teaspoon garlic powder
- 1 tablespoon olive oil

Filling

- 1 teaspoon olive oil
- 1 small shallot, sliced

- 1 cup spinach

- 5 cherry tomatoes, sliced

- 3 mushrooms, sliced

- ½ avocado, sliced

- 1 tablespoon parsley, chopped

Directions

1. In a large bowl, thoroughly combine the chickpea flour and flaxseeds. Add in water, lemon juice, tahini, salt, pepper, turmeric, oregano, garlic and whisk to combine. Set aside until mixture is thick, about 5-10 minutes.

2. In a medium skillet over medium-high heat, add teaspoon of olive oil, shallot, spinach, tomatoes and mushrooms. Quickly sauté for 3 minutes until spinach is slightly wilted. Remove and set aside.

3. Add tablespoon of olive oil to the medium skillet and heat over medium heat. Pour chickpea flour mixture into the pan and swirl to ensure it fully covers the bottom of the pan. Let cook for 5-7 minutes and then add the spinach mixture on one side. Fold omelet over and let cook another 2 minutes.

4. Remove from the pan and garnish with parsley before serving.

Mocha Pudding

Servings: 1

Total Time: 5 minutes plus 8 hours chill time

Ingredients

- 1 cup unsweetened almond milk

- ½ teaspoon vanilla extract

- ¼ cup chia seeds

- 2 tablespoons brewed coffee or espresso

- 1 teaspoon raw cacao

- 1 teaspoon cinnamon

- ½ small banana, sliced

- ¼ cup raspberries

- 1 tablespoon raw cacao nibs

Directions

1. Combine the almond milk, vanilla extract, chia seeds, coffee or espresso, cacao, and cinnamon in a small bowl (that has a cover) or a jar. Stir well to combine, cover and set in the fridge overnight.

2.   When ready to eat, top with banana, raspberries and cacao nibs.

Chocolate Chia Breakfast

Servings: 2

Total Time: 20 minutes plus 8 hours chill time

Ingredients

- 1 ½ cups unsweetened almond milk
- 1 teaspoon dried culinary lavender
- 1 teaspoon earl grey tea leaves
- 1 tablespoon raw honey
- 1 teaspoon vanilla extract
- ¼ cup raw cacao powder
- ¼ cup chia seeds
- 1 tablespoon cacao nibs
- 1 tablespoon walnuts, toasted and crushed

Directions

1.   In a small saucepan over medium heat, add the almond milk, lavender and tea. Let come to a gently boil and then turn heat off and put the lid on to allow lavender and tea to steep for 10 minutes.

2.   After milk has sat for 10 minutes, transfer to a medium-sized bowl and add in honey, vanilla and cacao. Stir in the chia seeds, cover and set in the fridge overnight.

3.   When ready to eat, top pudding with cacao nibs and toasted walnuts.

Zippy Ginger Breakfast Bars

Servings: 2 (1 bar each)

Total Time: 10 minutes plus 1 hour chill time

Ingredients

- ¼ cup raw almonds
- ¼ cup raw walnuts
- ½ cup dates, pitted, soaked 10 minutes and then drained
- 1 tablespoon fresh ginger, grated
- ¼ tablespoon cloves
- ¼ teaspoon cardamom
- ¼ teaspoon Himalayan salt

Directions

1.   Add all ingredients to a food processor and mix until a sticky dough forms.

2.   Shape dough into two equal sized bars and place on a plate in the fridge for at least 1 hour.

Breakfast Squash Bread

Servings: 2

Total Time: 40 minutes

Ingredients

- 1 cup almond meal
- 1 tablespoon flax meal
- 1/3 cup arrowroot flour
- ½ tablespoon chia seeds
- ½ teaspoon baking soda
- 1 tablespoon dried oregano
- ½ teaspoon Himalayan salt
- 1 egg
- ½ zucchini, finely grated
- ½ yellow squash, finely grated
- 2 tablespoons coconut milk
- 2 tablespoons coconut oil
- ½ teaspoon apple cider vinegar

Directions

1.   Preheat oven to 350°F/180°C. Line a mini loaf tin with parchment paper.

2.   In a medium-sized bowl, combine the almond meal, flax meal, arrowroot, chia seeds, baking soda, oregano and salt.

3.   Beat the egg in a large bowl and add the zucchini, squash, coconut milk, coconut oil and vinegar. Pour the dry ingredients into the large bowl with the wet ingredients and stir until well combined.

4.   Pour mixture into the prepared mini loaf pan and bake in the oven for 20-30 minutes or until lightly golden brown and cooked in the center.

Cherry Almond Bake

Servings: 2

Total Time: 50 minutes plus 30 minutes cooling

Ingredients

- 3 tablespoons unsweetened almond milk
- ¼ cup dates, pitted
- 1/3 cup almond meal
- ¾ teaspoon vanilla extract
- ¼ teaspoon almond extract
- ⅛ teaspoon Himalayan salt
- ¼ cup raw almonds, slivered and divided
- 1 ½ cups fresh cherries, pitted, divided
- 1 cup quinoa, cooked

Directions

1. Preheat oven to 350°F/180°C and line a small baking dish with parchment paper.

2.   Combine the almond milk, dates, almond meal, vanilla extract, almond extract, salt, half of the almonds and half of the cherries in a food processor or blender.

3.   Add mixture to a large bowl and stir in the quinoa. Pour into prepared baking dish and place remaining cherries and almonds on top.

4.   Bake in the oven for 45 minutes or until lightly browned on top.

5.   Remove from oven and let cool for 30 minutes before cutting into squares and serving.

Salmon & Cabbage Hash

Servings: 2

Total Time: 12 minutes

Ingredients

- 1 tablespoon olive oil

- 1 cup green cabbage, thinly shredded

- 1 cup sweet potato, shredded

- 3 green onions, thinly sliced, divided

- 4 ounces smoked salmon, flaked into bite-size pieces

- ¼ teaspoon black pepper, ground

- 1 tablespoon fresh dill, chopped

Directions

1.   In a medium-sized skillet over medium heat, add olive oil, cabbage, sweet potato and half the green onions. Sauté for 8 minutes until cabbage is soft and sweet potato is tender.

2.   Add smoked salmon, pepper and dill. Cook 2 minutes.

3.   Remove from heat and garnish with remaining green onions before serving.

Summer Medley Parfait

Servings: 2

Total Time: 10 minutes

Ingredients

- 1/3 cup raw cashews
- ½ tablespoon raw honey
- ½ teaspoon vanilla extract
- ¼ teaspoon almond extract
- 1 teaspoon lemon juice
- ⅛ teaspoon Himalayan salt
- 1 ½ cups strawberries, hulled, chopped and divided
- ½ tablespoon fresh mint, thinly sliced
- 1 cup honeydew, diced
- 1 teaspoon lemon zest
- 1/3 cup almonds, slivered and toasted

Directions

1. In a food processor, combine the drained cashews, raw honey, vanilla extract, almond extract, lemon juice and salt. Add

half of the strawberries and pulse until everything is combined thoroughly.

2.   Pour cashew mixture into serving bowls or glasses and top with remaining strawberries, mint, honeydew, lemon zest and almonds.

3.   Serve immediately.

Mexican Breakfast Toast

Servings: 2

Total Time: 5 minutes

Ingredients

- 2 slices sprouted bread, toasted
- 2 tablespoons hummus
- ½ cup spinach, chopped
- ¼ red onion, sliced
- ½ cup sprouts
- 1 avocado, thinly sliced
- ¼ teaspoon Himalayan salt

Spicy Yogurt

- 3 tablespoons unsweetened yogurt
- ½ lime, juiced
- 1 teaspoon cumin
- 1 teaspoon cayenne

Directions

1.   In a small bowl, prepare the Spicy Yogurt by combining all the Spicy Yogurt ingredients and whisking well to combine.

2.   Place toast slices on plates and spread a tablespoon of hummus on each. Place spinach on each slice and then Spicy Yogurt, red onion, sprouts and avocado. Sprinkle each with salt and serve.

Omega- Overnight Oats

Servings: 2

Total Time: 5 minutes

Ingredients

- 1 small ripe banana, mashed

- 1/3 cup rolled oats

- ¾ cup unsweetened almond milk

- ½ teaspoon vanilla extract

- ½ teaspoon cinnamon

- ¼ teaspoon nutmeg

- ⅛ teaspoon Himalayan salt

- 1 tablespoon chia seeds

- 1 tablespoon ground flaxseeds

- 1 teaspoon raw honey

- 1 tablespoon raw almonds, slivered and divided

- ¼ cup blackberries

Directions

1.   Place banana, oats, almond milk, vanilla, cinnamon, nutmeg, salt, chia seeds, flaxseeds, honey and half of the almonds in a medium-sized bowl with a lid or a jar. Stir well to combine and cover.

2.   Leave in the fridge overnight.

3.   When ready to eat, top with remaining almonds and the blackberries.

Broccoli Omelet

Servings: 2

Total Time: 15 minutes

Ingredients

- 12 ounces firm tofu
- 3 tablespoons unsweetened almond milk
- 3 tablespoons nutritional yeast
- 3 tablespoons tapioca starch
- 1 teaspoon Dijon mustard
- ¼ teaspoon turmeric
- ¼ teaspoon black pepper, crushed
- 2 tablespoons green onions

Filling

- 1 cup broccoli, steamed
- 1 shallot, sliced
- 2 tablespoons nutritional yeast

Directions

1.   Combine the tofu, almond milk, nutritional yeast, tapioca, mustard, turmeric and pepper in a food processor or blender until smooth.

2.   Heat a large, nonstick skillet over medium-high heat until very hot. Pour batter into the skillet and let cook for 7 minutes, being careful not to burn.

3.   Place Filling ingredients on one side of the omelet and flip over the other side to cover.

4.   Cook another 3 minutes and then transfer to a plate and garnish with green onions.

Tofu & Kale Tacos

Servings: 2

Total Time: 12 minutes

Ingredients

- 1 tablespoon coconut oil
- 7 ounces extra-firm tofu, drained
- 2 tablespoons nutritional yeast
- 1 teaspoon onion powder
- ¼ teaspoon turmeric
- 1 tablespoon coconut aminos
- 1 cup kale, thinly sliced
- 5 cherry tomatoes, halved
- 4 corn tortillas, warmed
- 1 tablespoon green onions, sliced
- 1 tablespoon cilantro, chopped
- 1 avocado, sliced

Directions

1.   Heat coconut oil in a medium-sized skillet over medium heat. Add tofu, nutritional yeast, onion powder, turmeric and coconut aminos. Cook 5 minutes.

2.   Add kale and cherry tomatoes to the skillet and cook another 5 minutes.

3.   Remove tofu kale mixture from the stove and divide among the tacos.

4.   Top with green onions, cilantro, avocado and serve.

Fruit Porridge

Servings: 2

Total Time: 25 minutes

Ingredients

- ½ cup whole buckwheat
- ½ cup water
- ½ cup unsweetened almond milk
- 1 tablespoon dried apricot, diced
- 2 tablespoons raisins
- 1 cinnamon stick
- ¼ teaspoon nutmeg
- ¼ teaspoon vanilla extract
- 1 teaspoon ground cardamom
- 1 tablespoon pomegranate seeds
- 1 tablespoon walnuts, toasted and crushed

Directions

1.   In a medium saucepan, add buckwheat, water, almond milk, apricot, raisins, cinnamon, nutmeg, vanilla and cardamom.

Bring to a boil and then allow to simmer, stir frequently for 20 minutes or until liquid is absorbed.

2.   Remove from heat, remove cinnamon stick and garnish with pomegranate seeds and walnuts before serving.

Breakfast Quinoa Salad

Servings: 2

Total Time: 20 minutes

Ingredients

- 1 teaspoon coconut oil

- ½ cup sweet potato, shredded

- ½ cup of red cabbage, shredded

- ½ cup cooked quinoa

- 2 cups spinach leaves, torn

- 12 cherry tomatoes, halved

- 1 avocado, sliced

Dressing

- 1 tablespoon olive oil

- 1 lemon, juiced

- 1 teaspoon Himalayan salt

- ½ teaspoon black pepper

- ½ teaspoon garlic powder

Directions

1.　　In a skillet over medium heat, warm coconut oil and add shredded sweet potato and red cabbage. Cook 7 minutes or until slightly softened.

2.　　Whisk together dressing ingredients in a small bowl.

3.　　Place quinoa, spinach and cherry tomatoes in a large bowl and pour sweet potato/cabbage mixture over. Stir to combine. Top with avocado and drizzle with dressing.

Carrot & Pineapple Cake Oatmeal

Servings: 2

Total Time: 20 minutes

Ingredients

- 1 carrot, shredded

- 2 cups water

- 1 cup rolled oats

- ½ pineapple, finely chopped

- ½ teaspoon cinnamon

- ½ teaspoon nutmeg

- ¼ teaspoon ginger powder

- ½ teaspoon vanilla extract

- ¼ cup almond milk

- 2 tablespoons walnuts, chopped

- 2 tablespoons shredded, unsweetened coconut

- 1 tablespoon raisins

Directions

1.　　In a saucepan over medium low heat, boil the shredded carrot with the water for 4-8 minutes.

2.　　Stir in oats, pineapple, cinnamon, nutmeg, ginger and vanilla extract. Simmer over low heat until liquid is gone and oats are soft, about 6-8 minutes.

3.　　Stir in almond milk, walnuts, coconut and raisins. Serve warm.

Warming Stew

Servings: 2

Total Time: 20 minutes

Ingredients

- 2 tablespoons olive oil
- 1 shallot, sliced
- 1 celery stick, diced
- 1 small carrot, diced
- 1 red bell pepper, diced
- 1 garlic clove, minced
- 1 cup green beans, sliced into 1 inch pieces
- 1 cup green cabbage, shredded
- 1 bay leaf
- 2 tablespoons dill, chopped
- 2 tablespoons parsley, chopped
- ½ teaspoon dried oregano
- 3 cups vegetable stock
- 2 cups spinach

- ½ teaspoon sea salt

- ¼ teaspoon black pepper

- 1 cup cooked brown rice

Directions

1.   Heat oil in a large stock pan and add shallot, celery, carrot, red bell pepper and garlic. Let cook 5 minutes or until softened, stirring occasionally.

2.   Add green beans and cabbage and cook another 5 minutes or until the cabbage has wilted. Stir in bay leaf, dill, parsley, oregano and then pour in the vegetable stock. Allow to come to a gentle simmer and stir in the spinach. Season with salt and pepper and serve over cooked brown rice.

Sweet Potato Avocado Toasts

Servings: 1

Total Time: 15 minutes

Ingredients

- 1 small sweet potato, sliced into 1 ½ inch slices

- ½ avocado, mashed

- 1 teaspoon garlic powder

- 1 teaspoon cumin

- ½ teaspoon Himalayan salt

- ½ teaspoon black pepper

- ½ tomato, sliced

- 1 teaspoon sesame seeds

Directions

1.   Place sweet potato slices in toaster and toast on high until slightly browned.

2.   In a bowl, mash the avocado, garlic powder, cumin, salt and pepper. Spread on top of sweet potato slices.

3.   Place tomato slices on top of the avocado mash and sprinkle with sesame seeds.

Smoky Sweet Potato & Kale Hash

Servings: 2

Total Time: 25 minutes

Ingredients

- 1 tablespoon coconut oil

- 1 shallot, sliced

- 1 medium sweet potato, diced

- 1 tart apple (such as Granny Smith), cored and diced

- 1 bunch kale (about 14 leaves), de-stemmed and sliced into ribbons

- 1 teaspoon smoked paprika

- ½ teaspoon Himalayan salt

- ¼ teaspoon pepper

Directions

1. Heat coconut oil in a skillet over medium-low heat. Add shallot and cook 2 minutes or until softened. Add sweet potato and cook 10 minutes being sure to flip potatoes about half way through.

2.   Add apple to the pan and cook an additional 2 minutes before tossing in the kale.

3.   Season with the paprika, salt and pepper.

4.   Cook until kale is slightly wilted and serve warm.

Chopped Breakfast Salad

Servings: 2

Total Time: 10 minutes

Ingredients

- 1 bunch kale, stems removed and sliced into thin ribbons
- 1 tablespoon olive oil
- 1 teaspoon Himalayan salt
- 1 lime, juiced
- ½ cup quinoa, cooked
- 1 cup watermelon, diced
- ½ cup pineapple, diced
- ½ cup raspberries
- 1 kiwi, diced
- ½ avocado, diced
- 2 tablespoons pepitas

Directions

1.　Place kale in a large bowl and add in the olive oil, salt and 1 tablespoon lime juice. Massage gently and set aside for 5 minutes.

2.　After 5 minutes, add quinoa, watermelon, pineapple, raspberries, kiwi, avocado and any remaining lime juice. Toss gently to combine.

3.　Sprinkle pepitas on top and serve.

Chai Spiced Breakfast Quinoa

Servings: 1

Total Time: 15 minutes

Ingredients

- ¼ cup quinoa
- ½ cup water
- ½ cup unsweetened almond milk
- ¼ teaspoon cinnamon
- ¼ teaspoon ground cardamom
- Pinch of ground ginger
- Pinch of ground clove
- 1 tablespoon chia seeds
- 1 teaspoon pepitas
- 1 teaspoon raw honey

Directions

1. Cook quinoa by combining water, almond milk, quinoa and spices in a medium saucepan over medium heat. Bring to a

boil and then reduce the heat to medium and let gently simmer for 5 minutes.

2. Once the water and milk are absorbed and quinoa is light and fluffy, stir in the chia seeds and pepitas. Transfer to a bowl and top with raw honey.

Chia Energy Parfait

Servings: 1

Total Time: 5 minutes

Ingredients

- ¾ cup unsweetened almond milk
- 3 tablespoons of chia seeds
- ½ teaspoon vanilla extract
- ¼ teaspoon cinnamon
- ¼ teaspoon nutmeg
- 2 tablespoons chopped cashews
- 1 tablespoon unsweetened shredded coconut flakes
- ¼ cup raspberries, slightly mashed
- ¼ cup mango, diced

Directions

1.   Combine almond milk, chia seeds, vanilla, cinnamon, nutmeg and cashews in a glass jar or bowl. Let sit overnight in the fridge.

2.	In the morning, layer on top the coconut flakes, raspberries and mango.

3.	Serve and enjoy!

Warm Apple Pie Breakfast Cereal

Servings: 2

Total Time: 5 minutes

Ingredients

- ½ cup quinoa

- 1 ½ cups unsweetened almond milk

- ¼ teaspoon vanilla

- ½ teaspoon cinnamon

- Pinch of allspice

- Pinch of nutmeg

- ½ lemon, juiced

- ¼ cup raisins

- 1 small Granny Smith apple, diced small

- ¼ cup raw almonds, chopped

- 1 teaspoon maple syrup, if desired

Directions

1.   Combine first 9 ingredients in a saucepan over medium heat. Bring to a gentle simmer then reduce heat to low and cook

until liquid is absorbed and quinoa is light and fluffy. Transfer to a bowl and top with almonds and maple syrup, if using.

Southwest Tofu Scramble

Servings: 2

Total Time: 15 minutes

Ingredients

- 1 tablespoon olive oil
- 2 shallots, sliced
- 1 red bell pepper, diced
- 1 cup broccoli florets
- ½ block firm tofu, cubed
- ½ teaspoon cumin
- ½ teaspoon paprika
- ½ teaspoon turmeric
- ¼ cup nutritional yeast
- ¼ teaspoon salt
- ¼ teaspoon pepper
- 3 tablespoons water
- 1 tablespoon cilantro
- 1 avocado, sliced

Directions

2.   Place olive oil in a skillet over medium heat. Add shallots, red bell pepper and broccoli florets. Cook 5 minutes.

3.   Add tofu to the pan, breaking up into crumbles with a spoon. Cook another 3 minutes.

4.   In a small bowl, mix together cumin, paprika, turmeric, yeast, salt, pepper & water. Pour into the skillet and toss evenly to coat. Cook until liquid evaporates and then stir in cilantro.

5.   Transfer to a plate and top with sliced avocado.

Fruity Chia Pots

Servings: 1

Total Time: 5 minutes

Ingredients

- ¼ cup chia seeds
- 1 cup unsweetened almond milk
- 1 teaspoon vanilla extract
- 1 tablespoon almonds
- 1 tablespoon cashews
- 3 tablespoons fresh blueberries
- 3 tablespoons fresh blackberries
- 2 tablespoons fresh raspberries
- 1 teaspoon raw honey (optional)

Directions

1. In a medium bowl or jar, combine chia seeds, almond milk and vanilla extract. Once fully combined, let sit overnight in the fridge.

2.   The next morning, stir in almonds, cashews, blueberries, blackberries and raspberries. Top with raw honey, if desired.

Sweet Potato Parfait

Servings: 1

Total Time: 35 minutes

Ingredients

- 1 cup unsweetened plain yogurt

- 1 teaspoon raw honey

- ½ teaspoon fresh ginger, grated

- ¼ teaspoon nutmeg

- ¼ teaspoon cinnamon

- 1 large sweet potato, roasted and flesh removed

- 1 tablespoon walnuts, chopped finely

- 1 tablespoon coconut flakes

Directions

1.   Mix together ¾ cup of yogurt, honey, ginger, nutmeg and cinnamon. Set aside.

2.   While still warm, mash the sweet potato flesh lightly.

3.　　In a deep bowl or jar, add some sweet potato, some yogurt, a few walnuts and coconut flakes. Repeat layers until all ingredients are used up.

Broccoli & Tofu Sandwich

Servings: 2

Total Time: 15 minutes

Ingredients

- 1 teaspoon coconut oil
- ½ cup broccoli, finely chopped
- 1 shallot, sliced
- ½ block firm tofu
- 1 teaspoon turmeric
- 1 teaspoon dried oregano
- 1 teaspoon garlic powder
- ¼ teaspoon Himalayan salt
- ¼ teaspoon pepper
- 2 tablespoons water
- 3 tablespoons nutritional yeast, divided
- 2 slices sprouted bread, toasted
- 1 avocado, sliced

Directions

1.   In a skillet, heat coconut oil and add broccoli and shallot to sauté. Crumble in tofu and cook 2 minutes.

2.   In a small bowl combine turmeric, oregano, garlic, salt, pepper, water and 1 ½ tablespoons of the yeast.

3.   Pour spice mixture over the tofu and broccoli mixture. Cook 3 minutes or until liquid is absorbed.

4.   Spoon tofu mixture over toasted bread, top with avocado and remaining nutritional yeast.

Nutty Overnight Oats

Servings: 2

Total Time: 10 minutes

Ingredients

- 1 cup uncooked oats

- 2 cups unsweetened almond milk

- 1 teaspoon vanilla extract

- 1 teaspoon cinnamon

- 1 teaspoon nutmeg

- ¼ teaspoon Himalayan salt

- 2 tablespoons almond butter

- 1 Granny Smith apple, cored and chopped

- 1 tablespoon hemp hearts (optional)

Directions

1. Mix together oats, almond milk, vanilla, cinnamon, nutmeg and salt. Divide this mixture equally in two jars. Combine mixture well and set in refrigerator overnight.

2.   In the morning, add almond butter, chopped apple and hemp hearts to each jar. Serve chilled.

Sunnyside Breakfast Bowl

Servings: 2

Total Time: 20 minutes

Ingredients

- 1 tablespoon coconut oil
- 1 teaspoon turmeric
- 2 shallots, diced
- 2 garlic cloves, minced
- ½ bunch kale, stems removed and leaves thinly sliced
- ¾ cup yellow split peas, thoroughly rinsed and drained
- 3 cups water
- ½ teaspoon Himalayan salt
- ½ cup grape tomatoes, halved
- 2 scallions, sliced
- 1 avocado, sliced
- 1 sliced breakfast radish
- 2 tablespoons pumpkin seeds, toasted

Directions

1.   In a medium saucepan heat coconut oil over medium heat and add turmeric, shallots, garlic and kale. Cook 5 minutes until kale is wilted. Add split peas and cook for 1 minute.

2.   Pour water and salt into the pan, cover and bring to a boil. Reduce heat to low and simmer for approximately 10 minutes.

3.   Divide amongst two bowls and top with tomatoes, scallions, avocado, radish and pumpkin seeds.

Turmeric Oats

Servings: 1

Total Time: 20 minutes

Ingredients

- ½ cup oats
- ¾ cup water
- ¼ cup unsweetened almond milk
- 1 teaspoon turmeric
- 1 teaspoon cinnamon
- ½ teaspoon Himalayan salt
- ¼ teaspoon black pepper, crushed
- 2 tablespoons raisins
- 2 tablespoons coconut flakes, toasted
- 1 tablespoon cacao nibs
- 1/3 cup raspberries

Directions

1.   In a small saucepan over medium-low heat, combine the oats, water, almond milk, turmeric, cinnamon, salt, pepper and raisins.

2.   Bring to a boil and then reduce heat to low and simmer until liquid is absorbed.

3.   Divide into bowls and top with coconut, cacao and raspberries.

Alkaline Breakfast Raw Mix

Servings: 2

Total Time: 10 minutes

Ingredients

- ¼ cup almonds, crushed
- ¼ cup pumpkin seeds
- ¼ cup walnuts, crushed
- ½ cup unsweetened coconut flakes
- 1/3 cup rolled oats (gluten-free)
- 2 teaspoons raisins
- 1 teaspoon sesame seeds
- 1 tablespoon raw honey
- 1 ½ tablespoons coconut oil, melted
- 1 teaspoon Himalayan salt
- ¼ teaspoon cinnamon
- ¼ teaspoon nutmeg
- 1 cup unsweetened almond milk
- 1 pear, cored and chopped

Directions

1.   Preheat oven to 300°F/150°C.

2.   In a bowl combine the almonds, pumpkin seeds, walnuts, coconut flakes, oats, raisins and sesame seeds.

3.   Pour the honey and coconut oil over the mixture and sprinkle with the salt, cinnamon and nutmeg. Toss to combine well and ensure everything is coated.

4.   Place mixtures on a parchment lined baking tray and bake for approximately 5 minutes, being careful not to burn.

5.   To serve, place mixture in bowls and top with almond milk and pear.

Mexican Breakfast Bowl

Servings: 2

Total Time: 10 minutes

Ingredients

- 1 ½ cups quinoa, cooked
- 2 tablespoons chia seeds
- 3 tablespoons scallions, thinly sliced
- 1 cup roasted red pepper, diced
- 1 cup cilantro, chopped
- 1 tablespoon nutritional yeast
- 1 teaspoon olive oil
- ½ lime, juiced
- ½ teaspoon Himalayan salt
- ½ teaspoon black pepper, crushed
- ¼ teaspoon cayenne
- ½ cup sprouts

Guacamole

- 1 avocado, pitted and mashed

- 1 shallot, diced

- 1 garlic clove, grated

- ½ lime, juiced

- 1 tablespoon cilantro, chopped

- 1 teaspoon cayenne

- 1 teaspoon cumin

- ½ teaspoon Himalayan salt

Directions

1.   In a large bowl, combine quinoa, chia seeds, scallions, red pepper, cilantro, nutritional yeast, olive oil, lime juice, salt, pepper and cayenne. Mix with a fork to combine well.

2.   Make Guacamole by adding all Guacamole ingredients to a small bowl and mixing together.

3.   Divide quinoa mixture into two bowls, top each with sprouts and the guacamole.

Avocado Zucchini Toast

Servings: 1

Total Time: 10 minutes

Ingredients

- 2 tablespoons olive oil
- 1 zucchini, grated
- ½ green bell pepper, finely diced
- 1 shallot, finely chopped
- 1 garlic clove, finely minced
- ¼ teaspoon dried oregano
- ¼ teaspoon dried thyme
- ¼ teaspoon dried basil
- ½ teaspoon Himalayan salt
- ½ avocado
- 2 slices gluten-free bread, toasted
- 1 tablespoon pumpkin seeds, toasted
- ¼ cup sprouts

Directions

1.   Heat olive oil in a small skillet over medium heat. Add the zucchini, bell pepper, shallot, garlic, oregano, thyme, basil and salt. Sauté 5 minutes and remove from heat.

2.   Mash the avocado and spread over the toast.

3.   Top with zucchini mixture, pumpkin seeds and sprouts.

Savory Asian Oatmeal

Servings: 2

Total Time: 15 minutes

Ingredients

- 1 cup rolled oats

- 2 cups water

- 1 tablespoon olive oil

- 2 tablespoons unsalted peanuts, crushed

- 3 tablespoons green onions, thinly sliced

- ½ jalapeno, seeds removed and diced

- 1 red bell pepper, seeded and diced

- 1 lime, juiced

- 1 teaspoon coconut aminos

- 1 teaspoon tamari

- ⅛ teaspoon chili powder

- ⅛ teaspoon cumin

- ⅛ teaspoon ground cloves

- 1/3 cup cilantro, chopped

- 1 teaspoon peanuts, crushed

Directions

1.   Bring oats and water to boil in a small saucepan over medium heat. Reduce heat to low and simmer about 8 minutes or until liquid is absorbed. Set aside.

2.   Heat olive oil in a medium skillet over medium-low heat. Add peanuts, green onions, jalapeno and bell pepper. Sauté 5 minutes or until soft.

3.   Stir in lime juice, coconut aminos, tamari and season with chili powder, cumin and cloves.

4.   Add oatmeal and cilantro to skillet and stir to combine.

5.   Divide into two bowls and top with peanuts.

Breakfast Fruit Crepes

Servings: 2

Total Time: 20 minutes

Ingredients

- 2 tablespoons ground flax
- 6 tablespoons water
- 1 cup buckwheat flour
- 1 tablespoon coconut oil, melted
- ½ teaspoon Himalayan salt
- ½ teaspoon coconut sugar
- ½ teaspoon vanilla extract
- ¼ teaspoon cinnamon
- 2 cups water
- 2 tablespoons ghee, melted
- 1/3 cup cashew butter
- 2 cups raspberries
- 1 tablespoon cacao nibs

Directions

1.   In a small bowl, whisk together ground flax and water. Place in the fridge for 15 minutes or until a gel is formed.

2.   In a blender, combine flax mixture, buckwheat, coconut oil, salt, sugar, vanilla, cinnamon and 2 cups water. Blend well and set aside.

3.   Brush ghee on a medium nonstick skillet and place over medium-low heat. Add some of the batter to pan and swirl around entire pan to create even layer. Cook 3 minutes on each side. Remove and repeat until batter is finished.

4.   In each crepe, add some of the cashew butter, raspberries and cacao nibs.

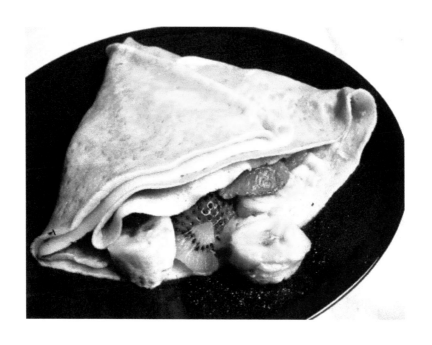